Getting Your Personal Brand Story Straight

ten exercises to help you get clear on the story you want to tell

Joanne Tombrakos

ISBN-13: 978-0-9840076-6-0

to my parents
without whom there would be no story for me to write

My Story
where this starts

This part of my story starts in August 2008 when I was *"reorganized"* out of my job at Time Warner. It was not the first time I had experienced being *"let go"* so the panic that often accompanies these situations did not consume me. I had learned first hand that my world would not end, but I also knew it would change. I just wasn't sure exactly how.

The next few months were no time to look for a job like the one I had. Financial markets were crashing. The media was doing their thing and perpetuating a dismal picture of doom and gloom. I suppose in hindsight I could have headed straight to the drain, drank too much or asked my doctor for a pharmaceutical to take the edge off, but instead I made a conscious effort not to take on the negative energy swirling around me. I'd lived through enough recessions and economic downturns that I knew we would eventually get to the other side of it. I also know enough about energy to know that letting the negativity consume me would not serve me. I needed to rise above it.

So I ate healthy, limited the alcohol intake, exercised a lot, finally made meditation and tapping a practice instead of a lark, surrounded myself with positive people and I wrote. I wrote a lot. I started a blog and from that blog came the unfolding of what would be the next chapter - one in which I would leave behind the structure of the career I had spent twenty-five years building.

None of it was easy, but all necessary to get me to where I am now, a personal brand advisor and business coach, digital and social media strategist and content creator who teaches Digital Marketing and Social Media at NYU, has written two books and writes - every day - for myself and for others.

I have found from my own personal experience and from working with others in career transitions that getting your personal brand story straight is hard work but critical to the process. It requires soul searching and asking the big questions no one wants to answer. You have to take a serious look at what you've done, what you're good at, what you like to do that you're good at and see how that can transfer to whatever you want to do next - in your industry or in a new one.

It also requires coming to terms with the bumps in the road and owning them instead of trying to sweep them under the carpet. The purpose of this workbook is to help you do that. At the end you will have the information to be able to encapsulate your story in as few as the 160 characters Twitter allots for a bio, using words that allow you to own it.

At times this will be fun. Other times, it will be confrontational. What's important to remember is that it's necessary - more so than ever in a digital world in which much of our story is left behind in a trail of breadcrumbs for all the world to see.

In order to get where you want to go, in order to get clear on what we like to call our "personal brand," in order to present yourself in a way that is authentic to you - online and offline - you need to get your story straight from where you stand today so you can get on to tomorrow and your next pages.

So let's get to it!

Joanne

> Your brand is what other people say about you
> when you're not in the room.
>
> Jeff Bezos, CEO and Founder, Amazon

Your story is more than the traditional elevator pitch.
It's what people are saying about you online and offline.

Getting Clear On Your Story
why it's essential for your personal brand

Getting clear on the story you want to tell is not an easy feat. It doesn't matter if your brand is a product or a service or your brand is you. It takes work and a lot of introspection. But the payoff is huge. When you're crystal clear on the story you want to tell, you're on the road to a successful brand!

For a long time we've been told to have our pitch ready for the day we find ourself standing in an elevator next to Oprah Winfrey so we can make the most of that precious moment in time. The idea is that in the seconds it takes for the elevator to move between floors the essence of who we are and why she would want to know us would be conveyed.

The problem with that is twofold. The first is that no one looks up from their phones much anymore in an elevator to notice who is standing next to them. The second is that while it is important to have a concise statement of who you are all about, your story is much more than a traditional elevator pitch.

Your story is the reputation you've built, where you've been and where you'd like to go. It's your work experience, your sense of style, where you went to school, the skills you've honed, your sense of humor and the places you've traveled to. It's every move you've made, every social media post you've shared and every nuance that has gotten you to where you are now. Your story is more an action verb than a noun.

Pay attention to the cracks.
That's where the light gets in.

Leonard Cohen

Your story is not blemish free.

Contrary to the image many portray of themselves on social media, we've all had our moments when things have not gone according to plan. We've been fired, reorganized out or demoted. We've lost as many jobs as we've won. We've gotten our dream job only to find out it's not the dream we thought it would be. We've tried to control our path only to find it's controlling us.

Many of us think that in telling our story we should only reveal the picture perfect version of ourselves. We forget that it's the scars and the bumps in the road that make us interesting. The key is learning how to tell it in a way that works for you so you can get to whatever is next.

Find out who you are and do it on purpose.

Dolly Parton

Getting your story straight requires some soul-searching.

Soul-searching is never easy. It requires answering the questions we avoid. It forces us to face up to our successes and failures and to owning both and it demands we ask ourselves what it is we want next.

That explains why we avoid it like the plague and why so few personal brands work in real life. You can't build a brand without a clear and engaging story.

In order to get your story straight you're going to have to take on this challenge. When you do take the time to get to the essence of who you are, the easier it is to get your story straight - online and offline.

You define your own life.
Don't let others write your script.

Oprah Winfrey

Get to the essence of the message you want to convey.

Our attention spans have shriveled to less than that of a goldfish which should come as no surprise given our addiction to our mobile phones and the constant distraction it offers.

What that means for any person, place or thing that has a message to share is that message must be crystal clear, concise and consistent across all platforms both online and offline. Without that clarity there is little chance of being heard.

Owning our story can be hard,
but not nearly as difficult as running from it.

Brene Brown

Your story is more than your bio.

A bio suitable for our LinkedIn profiles or our About page on our website is necessary, as is a resume. But your story is much more than that. It's the answers to the questions of who you are, what you do and who you serve. It's how you convey that story *online and offline.*

This workbook is designed to assist you in the process. My suggestion is to go in order and to complete all the exercises in a time frame that suits you. You may want to jump around and answer the easier stuff first. That's okay. Some of these exercises will be more challenging than others. Sometimes you may feel that you have already answered a question in an earlier exercise. That's done intentionally. The more you start writing it and saying it out loud, the easier it is to own it.

The brand is you, it is your story.

Diane Von Furstenberg

I already told you this will require some soul-searching so don't expect you can sit down one night and race through the whole workbook. The exercises you have the most trouble with are where you are likely to find your sweet spot.

The more information you get on paper, the clearer you'll get on your story and how you want to present it. This book is designed to be written in, however you may choose to get yourself a *"brand book"* that you can carry around with you so it's readily accessible to record ideas and insights as your muse bestows them on you. Brand books have worked for Diane Von Furstenberg. It's what she has said in her book, *The Woman I Wanted To Be,* she has used every time she is freshening her brand. They can work for you, too.

The more digitally connected we become,
the more disconnected we feel.
Our story helps to bridge that.

What Makes Good Story
show me, don't tell me

Marketing in the age of digital is about figuring out how to engage your product or service with your potential customer. Traditional or "push" marketing no longer works - that salesy sort of approach that says *buy me, buy me* and makes you want to run the other way. Marketers look for points of engagement so they can connect with their customers and build relationships with them so they want to buy from them and become repeat customers. All the paid advertising, remarketing and programmatic ad buys will do little if your brand doesn't resonate. Good marketers use story to do that.

The same holds true for you.

Story is what connects us.

It's not our resume or a long list of our skills and experience, but the story of how all that came to be that connects us with other humans. The research tells us that good story actually makes us feel better. It releases oxytocin - also called the "love hormone" - the same chemical that is released when we feel connected or fall in love.

Story makes us human and in a world in which the more digitally connected we get the more disconnected from each other we feel, it becomes more important than ever.

Technology is just the means, not the end in itself.
The story is what's really at stake.

Michael Margolis

Our bio is not enough.

We need well written, clear and concise bios, but we need our story more. Besides, you can't write a really good bio without clarity around your personal story and you can't grow your personal brand without knowing how you want to tell that story - online and offline.

Good story includes well-developed characters with a point of view, conflict and resolution. In the case of personal branding you are that character. The "plot" or your journey from where you started to where you are now is important but the more developed your character is portrayed, the more engaged we will be.

Some stories are more plot driven. Others are more character driven. In the case of the personal brand the most engaging stories will be character driven.

What you do in the world serves to solve a problem someone else has. Your story is showing us how you do that.

To be a person is to have a story to tell.

Isak Dinesen

"But I have no story."

I hear that all the time. *I'm boring. Her life is more interesting than mine. Look at all he's accomplished. Blah. Blah. Blah.*

We all have a story. We all have something remarkable about us. The hard part is coming to terms with not just the good parts, but the blemishes and owning the fact that it is the twists and turns we have navigated that make us the most interesting.

The Basic Three
just three questions

We'll start with the basics. Remember there are no right or wrong answers here. You may find as you go through the workbook you will come back to this and rework some of what you've written. You may find I ask you this question again - and again - and again - just to see if you say the same thing or if the answers are evolving. But for now, take a first stab while applying the cardinal rule of brainstorming - no self-censure and no judgments on what you write - or what you don't write.

Who are you?

What do you do?

Why do you do it?

The 7 Questions
Stanislavski's famous question

The great acting teacher, Konstantin Stanislavski believed an actor needed to get inside the head of their character so they could better understand them. He developed seven fundamental questions he thought needed to be asked when approaching a character one might play.

In order to get your own story straight, it's going to be necessary to get inside your own head - which is never as easy as it sounds.

Ask yourself his seven questions.

Who am I?

Where am I?

When is this?

What do I want?

Why do I want this?

How will I achieve my goal?

What must I overcome?

Nothing But Words
because words have power

Write your name in the circle below.

At the end of each arrow write a word or phrase that you think best describes you and what you bring to the table.

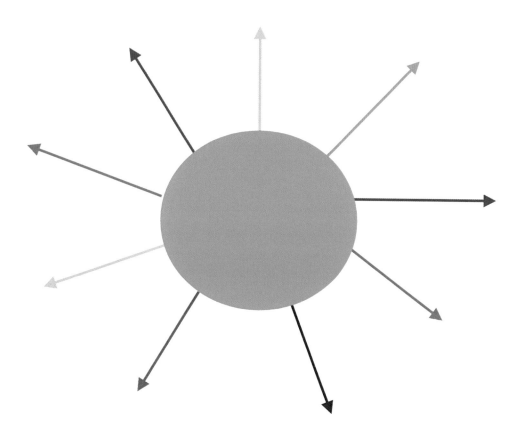

At a loss for words?

Here are some suggestions that might jog that brain! It's not an all-inclusive list. Use whatever works best for you and add on ones of your own!

bold	entrepreneurial	cutting-edge	flexible	focused
dynamic	engaging	expressive	loyal	results-oriented
perceptive	inventive	untraditional	self-motivated	insightful
agile	curious	adaptable	dependable	trustworthy
analytical	driven	detail oriented	organized	proactive
open-minded	ambitious	leader	initiator	problem solver
competititve	creative thinker	forward thinking	approachable	conservative

Remember - this is about creating *your* unique presence.

Keywords And Titles
what will you call yourself?

Keywords are essential in the digital world. They are the words or phrases someone might type into a Google search bar to find you or someone like you. Incorporating keywords into our story and title are the clues we give so Google's algorithms help us to be found. Before we start thinking about what to call ourselves let's think about the keywords or keyword phrases you think someone would type into a search engine to find someone like you.

Keywords are critical to the process, especially when making full use of a social platform like LinkedIn. Keywords are essential if we want recruiters and business prospects to find us.

For Advanced Players only. Google offers a free Keyword planner tool to assist you. This will be especially helpful for those who desire to be influencers and thought leaders with the intention of creating content for social media sharing.

All you need to do is type in one word or phrase that tells us what you do and Google's tool will offer suggestions based on recent search results. For example when I type in personal brand advisor I immediately discover other options which suggest personal branding is a more common search term.

https://ads.google.com/home/tools/keyword-planner/

Now it's your turn.

List 5 —10 keywords or keyword phrases that you think someone would use to find you.

Every story needs a title.

Most writers start their stories with a working title. Often by the time they're done, that title has changed. That may happen for you as well. One of the beauties of life in the digital age is that you can change or tweak your titles in real time.

I always suggest writing three titles. At least one should include one of those keywords you uncovered to help you get discovered in searches. Be as creative or playful as you like with the other two - as long as they make a statement about who you are and what you do.

For example, I use Storyteller as one of my titles. For me this was the one word that encompassed three of my skills: writing, selling and teaching as I have always believed good selling and good teaching require the ability to tell good story. The bonus on this is that it has also proved to be a conversation piece when I meet someone new.

Having trouble?

The Silicon Valley job title generator might spur your creativity. Even if you're not a Silicon Valley type this could give you some ideas!

It's also smart to do some research. Search for people who do what you do or do what you want to do on LinkedIn and see what they're calling themselves.

http://siliconvalleyjobtitlegenerator.tumblr.com

Write 6-8 possible titles you might want to call yourself.

Let them sit for a while and when you're ready, come back and narrow them down to 2-3 you want to call your own.

Solicit Help!

see you as others see you

Ask 6 people you know for their input.

We don't always see ourselves as others do so it's good to ask those that know us what they think.

Make a list of six people you know from varying areas of your life that you can solicit help from. My only stipulation is that you try to avoid parents and significant others - unless you happen to work with them.

Email them a note.

Tell them you're working on getting your personal brand story straight and you need their help in answering these questions.

√ What do they see as your best quality?

√ What do they see you bring to the table?

√ What do they admire about you?

√ What do they see for you?

Now that you've got this information....

Schedule yourself some alone time. Read through each with an open mind. Look for common threads. Highlight what resonates most with you. Look for feedback that surprised you.

Remember - you don't have to do anything with this new information if you don't want to. The point is for you to get more information about how you are perceived through the eyes of others who know you well enough to have a viewpoint. But before you choose to hit the delete button on their responses take some notes!

What resonated the most?

What surprised you?

What ideas has this sparked for your personal brand?

Consider independent third party feedback.

Sometimes you want your feedback from an independent third party. There are many to choose from, but the one I recommend is called The Fascination Advantage Assessment and was created by Sally Hogshead.

Sally is well known in her field and has written several books on the subject of how business and personal brands fascinate, including *How The World Sees You*. She and her team identified seven primary triggers of fascination that include: passion, mystique, prestige, power, innovation, alert, and trust.

From these triggers they created a set of archetypes to help you understand which of these is how *you* most fascinate others so you can use them to your advantage.

The assessment is relatively inexpensive and quick to take but leaves you with a lot of really useful information that can help you get your story straight and show you how you can deliver that story in a way that fascinates!

One of the things I love about her work is that she advocates using this information to become more of who you are, not to be someone you think you should be.

I've used this as an exercise with my graduate students for years and will attest that they find the results overwhelmingly accurate.

https://www.howtofascinate.com/store/fascination-advantage-assessment

For extra credit

Watch Sally's Ted Talk on how all markets are like online dating markets. Just one note - the video was produced in 2011 and the names of some of the triggers have since changed as well as the length of our attention spans but the message is still powerful!

https://www.youtube.com/watch?v=nGoWiP5ux1Q

Write your independent third party results here.

The Pinterest Board
using social media to organize

Every semester for their midterm presentation I require my NYU grad students to present themselves as a brand to the class in three minutes. The idea is to take all the tools they're learning to use for products and services and apply it to themselves.

This is challenging in more ways than one. For these young millennials this is often the first time they've had to think this through and ask themselves the tough questions about who they are, what they do and whom they serve. Because they're in a marketing degree program I also ask them to be as creative as possible.

Several years ago, I had a student who decided to present her personal brand through a series of Pinterest boards. It made perfect sense for her as she was very visual and had a flair for design. Her well thought out presentation got her an A and it also gave me an idea. Using Pinterest boards is a great way to gain clarity around the different facets of what makes up your personal brand!

Pinterest is different than other social media in that it's format is set up to organize by category - or in this case the many sides of what makes up personal and professional you. Keep in mind there are no hard and fast rules. This is just another opportunity for you to drill down to the specifics of what makes your story yours.

Plan your Pinterest Boards.

Write in the subject titles that you might use to create your boards.

Story Starter #7
more questions

The more questions you ask yourself the more clarity you will have. Even if some of these questions seem like ones you've answered already, remember that I've done that intentionally and it's to your benefit to answer them again.

√ who are you?

√ where do you come from?

√ what do you do?

√ why do you do it?

√ how do you do it?

√ whom do you serve?

√ what's your purpose?

√ what are you good at?

√ where have you been?

√ what adventures have you embarked on?

√ what mark do you want to make on the world?

√ what makes you smile?

√ how do you fascinate others?

√ what makes you remarkable?
(NOTE: there is something remarkable about each and every one of us!)

Above all, be the heroine of your life,
not the victim.

Norah Ephron

The Tag Line
promotional bumpers and soundbites

Even if you're not a marketer, tag lines, promotional bumpers, teasers and soundbites are a part of your daily life. You just might not have realized it.

If you've ever listened to a radio station you've heard promotional bumpers, those little snippets of audio and underlying music that historically buffer transitions between program segments in between commercials reminding you of the station you are listening to and why.

Perhaps one of the more famous is that of 1010Wins, New York's all news radio station. *"You give us twenty-two minutes, we'll give you the world!"*

In just a few words with bit of music underneath we know the essence of their brand story and what to expect - a look at news around the world in just twenty-two minutes.

Tag lines are used to differentiate you from the competition.

- Nike's familiar swoosh reads *"Just Do It."*

- L'Oreal Paris is *"Because you're worth it."*

- Hertz is *"#1"* but Avis says *"we try harder."*

- Bounty uses *"the quicker picker upper."*

Whether it's a promotional bumper or a tag line, these soundbites offer us something about the brand that tells us how they can help and what makes them different from the competition in as few words as possible. They work for personal brands too.

But this sounds just like an elevator pitch.

Here's the thing about elevator pitches. First of all the title makes no sense in today's world. No one looks up from their phone long enough to have a conversation in an elevator. Secondly, pitch implies you are selling something and trying to make something happen. Taglines are statements that help us to understand who you are and what you do.

Taglines are more useful to getting your story straight.

A tagline or promotional bumper is a statement of who you are and how you help solve a problem that exists. It can be used at a networking event, on a website or simply written on a sticky note on your computer to remind yourself of what the essence of your brand is.

As an example, my current tag line reads: *"I help you tell your story and build your brand and business - digital first."*

Note that I use the word current. In today's environment we can be fluid with our brand and adjust and tweak as we progress our careers.

Write your tagline.

Now it's your turn to brainstorm some taglines. Try for five to ten options and write them in the spaces provided. The easiest way is to start with what you do and how you help solve a problem. Don't overthink this. Just do it. After you have them down, step away for a bit and come back later. That's when you can circle the ones that really speak to you.

If you're having trouble with that second part, record your options so you can hear how it sounds!

....

....

....

....

....

....

....

....

Log Lines
telling your story with the most impact

If you've ever tried to pitch a script to someone in the movie industry, you know you have a very short window in which to encapsulate the plot of your story and capture their attention. The tool they used long before Twitter and 140 character soundbites became famous is called a log line.

A log line is a brief description of the plot of your story - in this case your personal brand story.

It involves an emotional hook and a twist of irony.
It organizes a story in the briefest form possible while retaining the strongest emotional effect.

Log Lines include:

Set up: empathy for the central character
Dilemma: at least two solutions
Action: how the character pursues the goal.
Goal: with a twist of irony.

Some examples of Log Lines.

A young man and woman from different social classes fall in love aboard an ill-fated voyage at sea. *Titanic*

An epic tale of a 1940s New York Mafia family and their struggle to protect their empire, as the leadership switches from the father to his youngest son. *The Godfather*

A cutthroat businessman who wants to remain detached needs a date for some social engagement; he hires a beautiful prostitute he meets...only to fall in love with her. *Pretty Woman.*

A lovestruck and broke woman is tasked as her best friend's maid of honor, and must complete all the usual rituals with a group of oddball bridesmaids. *Bridesmaids.*

When a corporate executive with a tidy life and comfortable income loses her job at the beginning of the worst economic downturn in modern history, she embarks on a journey of reinvention to discover, her truth, happiness, and financial success as a storyteller, consultant and educator. *Me!*

The Log Line Template

It's time to give this a try!

This can be very effective - especially if you are redesigning, reinventing and/or trying to come to terms with a bump or two in the road and trying to figure out how you are going to use that to your advantage. At the same time it forces you to envision where you want to go.

Just remember that this exercise is NOT designed for you to post on your LinkedIN profile.

It is to help you get more information so you can not only get your personal brand story straight, but start learning to own it.

What makes you different or weird,
that's your strength.

Meryl Streep

When [**INCITING INCIDENT OCCURS**],

a [SPECIFIC PROTAGONIST- **YOU**]

must [**OBJECTIVE**],

or else [**STAKES**].

The only thing worse than being blind
is having sight but no vision.

Helen Keller

The Manifesto
the final stretch

A manifesto is defined as a mission statement or platform.

If you don't know where you want to go and how you want to get there chances are you're going nowhere. Writing a manifesto is an exercise to get clear on that direction.

It's more than a vision board.

Vision boards are also great exercises. But the purpose of writing a manifesto is to force you to put words around whatever it is you want to do, be or create and since this workbook is about getting your story straight, we need words.

How to do it.

- Get out a blank sheet of paper or write in the spaces provided here.
- Read the questions that follow this section.
- Set a timer for an hour.
- Work without interruption. No email, phones, texts.
- Brainstorm. Words. Phrases. Sentences.
- Write down whatever comes up for you.
- Remember the rules of brainstorming are uncensored free flow.
- There are no right or wrong answers.
- You can and will edit later.
- Do not stop until the timer goes off.
- Walk away from what you have so far and let it simmer.
- Schedule your next session on your calendar.
- Read out loud what you have, then set that timer again.
- Add and delete, reviewing the question list throughout.
- Repeat as needed until you feel your manifesto is complete.

- What message do you want to convey to the world?

- What do you strive to do each day?

- What do you believe in?

- What are the principles you live by?

- What are your intentions?

- How do you/your business want to change the world?

Other advice and tips.

- Use strong language.

- Don't dismiss this as frivolous.

- If you really want to get clear on your story this will help.

- Be authentic.

- Try and revisit your manifesto every few months.

- Consider creating a word cloud to make your manifesto visual using a free tool like https://www.wordclouds.com or http://www.wordle.net.

My Manifesto

This is the manifesto I wrote in May 2011. I'm happy to say, I'm still on track.

It's not enough to know your story.
You have to own it.

Your bio is not your story.
Your story is the engaging part of your bio.

Drafting Your Bio
pulling it all together

In the beginning of this workbook, I told you your story is much more than your bio or your resume. The goal was that by now you would have more clarity on that story than you did before. I hope you've found that to be true.

But you do still need that bio and it's time to take all the information you've gathered from these exercises and write your first draft.

Your bio should:

- ☐ have an engaging first line
- ☐ include appropriate keywords so you are "discoverable"
- ☐ be concise, well-written and to the point
- ☐ sound like you
- ☐ be easy to read - no jargon or gobbledygook
- ☐ be easy to read - people don't read online - they scan!
- ☐ tell just enough of your story that makes us want to know more
- ☐ be grammatically correct with no spelling errors!

You should have several versions for different platforms.

- ☐ a long version - 150 - 300 words for platforms like LinkedIn
- ☐ LinkedIn currently has a 2000 character limit (approx. 300 words)
- ☐ a short version - 50-75 words
- ☐ a 160 character version for Twitter and Instagram
- ☐ first person versions when you want to be more personal
- ☐ third person versions when you want to be more professional

Remember - this is your *first* draft.

It will need a few revisions before it's ready to go! If you're really having trouble, you can outsource a good copywriter. Just make sure they take some time to know *you* so they write in *your* voice and not theirs.

Great opening lines

The first line of your bio will determine whether or not someone will keep reading. Think of this in the same way you would a good book or a movie. That opening scene will either keep you hooked or send you scrolling somewhere else.

For example in his opening line on Linkedin, David Meerman Scott, a globally recognized marketing and sales expert starts with a line about getting fired.

Best selling author and keynote speaker, Ann Handley, begins by telling us she is the world's first Chief Content Officer. Barbara Stanny Huson, Wealth Coach and best selling financial author states her mission in life is to revolutionize a woman's relationship with money and power. Gloria Feldt, Co-founder and President of Take the Lead starts with the mission of the organization she helped to found.

On Linkedin I start by using my tag line and telling you what I do, help you tell your story, build your brand and business, digital-first, but if you remember back to the beginning of this workbook I started by telling you that in 2008 I lost my job.

There are many ways to approach this and the platform on which your bio will reside factors in, but what is most important to ask yourself is if your opening line engages people to read more or bores them and sends them on their way.

One last tip - when writing this for anything online, make sure to include a keyword or two in that first section to help those algorithms do their job in your favor.

Today you are you
That is truer than true
There is no one alive
Who is Youer Than You!

Dr. Seuss

The End Is The Beginning
it all starts now

Good story generally has a beginning, a middle and an end. Great story ends with the beginning of something we can't quite predict but leaves us satisfied enough that we know we're on the right track.

That's where I hope this finds you - owning the story of where you've been and where you want to go and able to articulate it in 160 characters or 300 words - on social media, in real life and in a letter of introduction or a full fledged bio. And it's all you, in your own authentic voice.

Your personal brand story is not a destination.
It is a living, breathing organism.
You are writing new pages every day.
It will evolve.
You need to remain agile and open to the change.

end notes
a few more things before I go

My hope is that this workbook has helped you on this leg of your personal branding journey. If you need more help - either in advisement or in editing your personal brand story, find me on social media @joannetombrakos or visit my website, https://joannetombrakos.com and drop me a note.

to be continued,

About the author

Joanne Tombrakos is the Founder and Chief Storyteller at One Woman's Eye Consulting and Training where she helps build brands, digital first. Considered a SME in personal branding, content marketing and social media, she is also an Assistant Professor at NYU where she has been teaching Digital Marketing, Social Media and Real World Courses in the MS in the Integrated Marketing Program since 2013 as well as at The Katz School of Business at Yeshiva University. In a previous life she held senior management positions in media sales for CBS Radio and Time Warner Cable.

Above all, she is a writer who learned how to deliver a powerful and engaging message using a limited number of words when she was selling country music radio in the 80's and had to write Ad copy for her clients. Her corporate background in media sales connected her with a variety of business in multiple sectors and provides unique insight that benefit her clients. She is also the author of *The Secrets They Kept, It Takes An Egg Timer, A Guide To Creating The Time For Your Life,* this workbook and the publisher of an almost weekly newsletter, *One Woman's Eye,* tips, tools and inspiration to help you manage digital so it doesn't manage you.

In her spare time, *and trust me that she makes sure that exists,* you can find her sipping a glass of wine, losing herself in a good book or movie and spending time with those in her life who matter most.

Made in the USA
Las Vegas, NV
02 February 2022

42877110R00062